Kingfisher Books, Grisewood & Dempsey Ltd,
Elsley House, 24-30 Great Titchfield Street,
London W1P 7AD

First published in 1993 by Kingfisher Books
2 4 6 8 10 9 7 5 3 1

Material in this edition was previously published by
Kingfisher Books in *On the Move: Tractor* in 1990.

© Grisewood & Dempsey Ltd 1990, 1993

Series editor: Veronica Pennycook
Series designer: Terry Woodley
Typeset in 3B2
Phototypeset by SPAN
Printed in Great Britain by
BPCC Paulton Books Limited

LITTLE LIBRARY

The Farm Tractor

Angela Royston

Illustrated by Jane Gedye

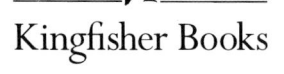

Kingfisher Books

In this book

This book is all about a tractor.
The type of tractor in the story is
a John Deere 2850.

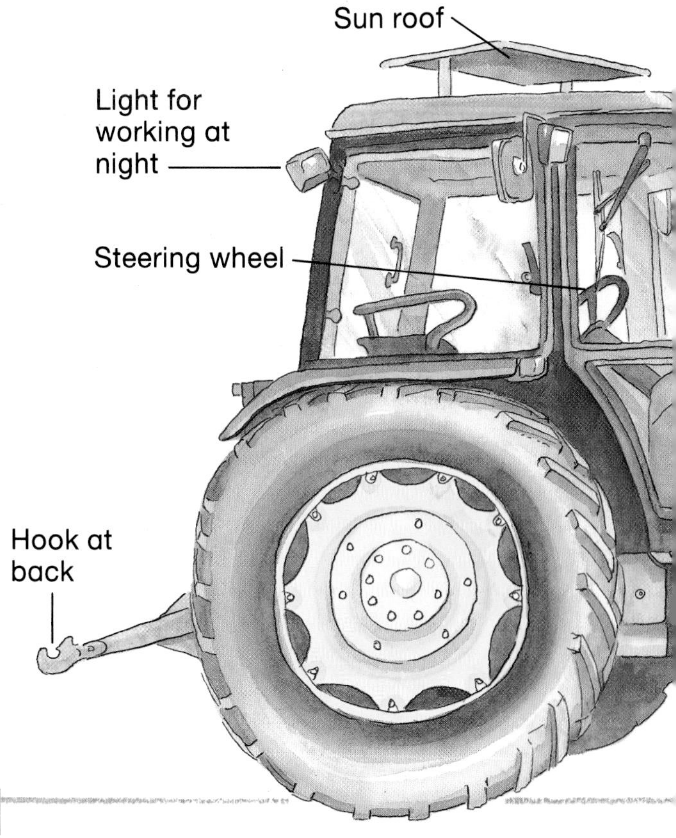

Sun roof

Light for
working at
night

Steering wheel

Hook at
back

Tractors are used on the farm all year round to pull heavy carts and machinery. Farmers use them for many different jobs, such as ploughing fields, sowing seed and harvesting crops.

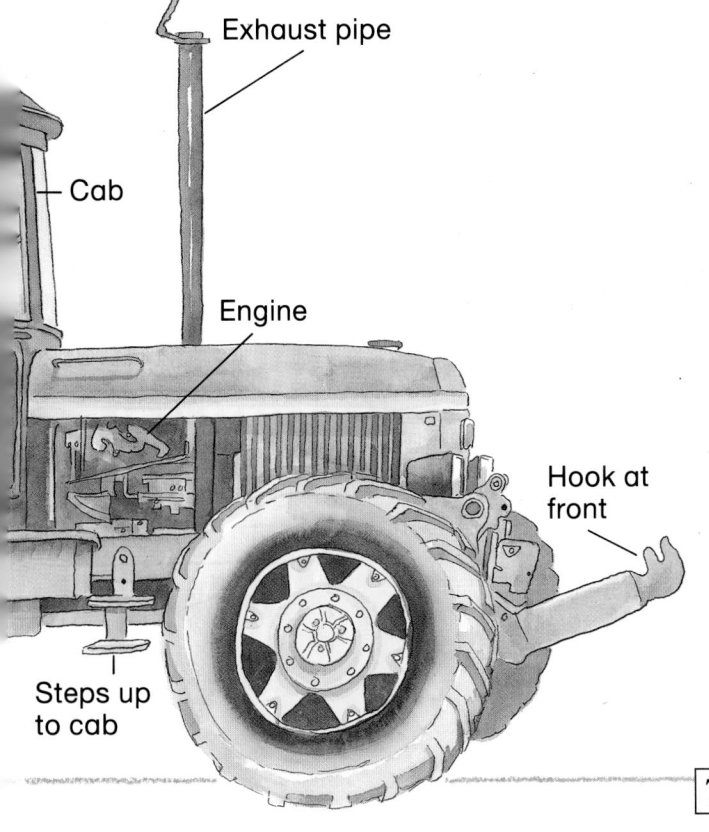

Exhaust pipe

Cab

Engine

Hook at front

Steps up to cab

A winter morning

Every morning Joe the farmer sets off early to feed the pigs. He hooks a trailer on to the tractor and drives over to the barn.

There he loads up the trailer with two large bags of pig feed and some bales of straw. The straw keeps the pigs warm during the cold winter nights. Joe climbs back into his cab and sets off down the lane to the pigs' field.

Stuck in the mud

When Joe tries to drive the tractor
into the pigs' field the wheels sink
down into the thick mud.

Joe puts his foot down hard on
the accelerator. The front wheels
spin, spattering mud everywhere.
At last the big wheels start to grip
and the tractor moves forwards.

The pigs are hungry and grunt excitedly as Joe fills their troughs with feed. They gather round him snuffling and pushing their snouts into the trough.

Then Joe unloads the new straw and spreads some out inside all the pig huts.

Cutting the grass

It's spring and the grass is ready to be cut. Joe hooks up the mower to the tractor. At the field, he pulls a lever in the cab to make the mower cut the grass.

When he's finished cutting the grass, Joe leaves it to dry in the sun. Then after a few days he turns it over. Slowly, the grass dries and turns into hay.

Now Joe hooks the big baling machine to the tractor and tows it out to the hay field.

Baling the hay

Joe drives the baling machine slowly across the field. It picks up the hay and presses it into square bales. Then the machine ties each bale with string and pushes it out on to the field.

In the afternoon the sky clouds over. Cath and Jim help Joe bring in the hay before the rain arrives and spoils it. They hurry to load the bales on to a trailer and Cath's tractor pulls load after load to the barn. The rain starts as they are finishing their last load. "We've just made it!" says Cath.

Crop spraying

The hay is safely in, but during the good weather greenfly have hatched on the growing wheat.

Joe decides to kill them with insecticide before they spoil the crop. He pours water and insecticide into the sprayer and then joins it to the tractor.

When he reaches the field of wheat, he unfolds the long boom arms on the sprayer. He drives backwards and forwards through the crop, letting a fine spray of insecticide fall on the greenfly. It takes him a whole afternoon to finish the spraying.

Harvest time

It is nearly the end of the summer and the wheat is yellow and ripe. Joe hopes the warm weather will last for a few more days so he can harvest the wheat.

He drives a big combine harvester. It has long blades in front that cut the wheat stalks.

The cut wheat goes into the combine harvester. Inside, the wheat grains are separated from the stalks and the chaff.

The grains are then poured out of the long arm on the side of the combine and fall into a trailer. The stalks and chaff are dropped back on to the field.

Into the hopper

Cath drives the tractor and the trailer full of grain back to the farm and tips it into a big hopper where it's left to dry. She then goes back for the next load.

When Joe has finished cutting
all the wheat, he attaches the
baling machine to the tractor and
makes the straw that's left on the
field into bales.

Ploughing

The weeks pass and autumn comes. The crops have been gathered and all the straw has been baled and stored. Now it's time to plough the fields, ready to sow a new crop for next year.

As Joe pulls the plough its sharp blades cut into the earth and turn over the soil, making deep furrows. The roots of this year's plants are pulled up and mixed in with the soil. Soon the yellow field has changed to brown.

Sowing the seed

The next morning Joe goes back to the ploughed field. There, he fastens up a drill to the back of the tractor and fills the seed box with seeds and fertilizer to help the seeds grow.

As Joe drives the tractor up and down, the drill scratches shallow lines in the earth and the seeds trickle into them. There is a harrow at the back of the drill which rakes soil over the seeds. "I hope these grow into a good crop like this year's," thinks Joe.

Time for a service

It is winter again. There is not so much work for the tractor to do now, so Joe decides to clean it and service the engine. He scrapes off the mud and hoses it down.

He checks the engine, drains the old dirty oil and pours in new oil. "This tractor should keep going for a few years yet," thinks Joe, as he gets it ready for another busy spring and summer.

Some special words

Accelerator   The lever that makes the engine run faster or slower.

Chaff   The ears of wheat after the grain has been taken out.

Combine harvester   A machine that cuts wheat and separates the grain from the stalks and chaff.

Hopper   An open box in which grain is stored.

Service   A regular check that makes sure all the parts of an engine are working well.

Straw   Stalks of wheat after it has been cut.

Index

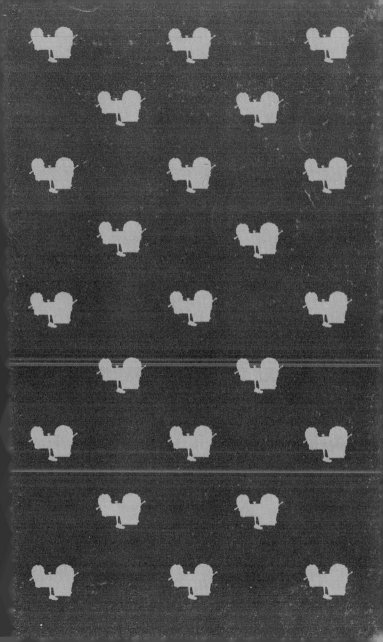